WHOO STANK THE CAJUN SKUNK

WRITTEN BY KEDOSKEE

ISBN: 979-8-218-23629-8

Published by Writersclique

FIRST DAY JITTERS

Once upon a time, in a forest far away, lived a little skunk named Whoo Stank. Whoo Stank was a unique creature, unlike any other skunk in the forest; he didn't smell bad at all! His parents, who were both skunks too, were always proud of their little Whoo Stank and his special trait. They loved him dearly and always encouraged him to be himself, no matter what others might think.....

Whoo Stank lived with his parents in a cozy burrow under a big oak tree. His home was decorated with colorful flowers and leaves that his mother, a talented gardener, had planted. Whoo Stank's father was a skilled woodcarver and had carved a beautiful wooden sign that read "Whoo Stank's Home" that hung over the entrance to their burrow.

Whoo Stank was about to start his first day of school, and he was feeling nervous. He had never been away from his parents and had never made any friends before. "What if nobody likes me because I'm different?" he asked his parents, worry etched on his little face.

His parents, sensing his anxiety, hugged him tightly and reassured him that he was special just the way he was. "Don't worry, Whoo Stank," said his mother, "you are unique, and that is something to be proud of." His father added, "Just be yourself, and you will make friends in no time."

With his parents' loving words in his heart, Whoo Stank set off for his first day of school. The forest was bustling with excitement as all the animals were preparing for the new school year. Whoo Stank could see the rabbits hopping around, the squirrels gathering nuts, and the birds chirping merrily in the trees.

As Whoo Stank walked towards the school, he felt a little scared but also excited to make new friends. He wondered if he would find someone who would accept him for who he was, despite his unique trait.

Whoo Stank's school was located in a lush, green area surrounded by tall trees and a babbling brook. The school building was made of wooden planks and had a thatched roof, giving it a cozy, rustic feel. As Whoo Stank stepped into the classroom, he saw that it was just as charming as the exterior. The walls were adorned with colorful posters and artwork created by previous students. The desks and chairs were made of polished wood and arranged neatly in rows, with a large chalkboard at the front of the room. Sunlight streamed in through the open windows, casting a warm glow on everything inside. Despite feeling nervous, Whoo Stank couldn't help but feel a sense of wonder as he looked around the room.

Whoo Stank took a deep breath. As he looked around, he noticed that all eyes were on him. The other students, a mix of rabbits, squirrels, and even a few baby bears, were whispering amongst themselves and pointing in his direction.

Feeling a little self-conscious, Whoo Stank made his way to an empty desk at the back of the room. But as he sat down, he couldn't shake the feeling that he didn't belong.

Just then, a little baby crocodile with a big smile on his face waddled up to Whoo Stank. "Hi there! I'm Toots," he said cheerfully. "Do you want to sit with me?"

Whoo Stank's heart lifted as he looked at Toots' friendly face. "Yes, please!" he said, relieved to have found a friend.

Just then, the classroom door swung open, and in walked their teacher, Ms. Ollie. She had a kind face and wore a brightly colored scarf around her neck.

"Good morning, class!" Ms. Ollie said in a cheerful voice. "Welcome to the first day of school. I'm so excited to get to know each and every one of you."

As Ms. Ollie began to go over the rules of the classroom, Whoo Stank couldn't help but feel grateful for Toots' company. He glanced around the room and noticed that no one else seemed to want to sit with him.

But Ms. Ollie soon put an end to that. "Now, I want everyone to remember that this is a safe place," she said firmly. "Everyone is equal here, and we welcome and accept everyone, no matter their differences." she added "and class, always remember; When we are not afraid, we can feel hopeful."

Whoo Stank felt a surge of warmth in his chest as he heard Ms. Mimi's words. He knew he had found a special place where he would be accepted for who he was. And with Toots by his side, he felt more confident than ever before.

FRIENDS STICK TOGETHER

WHOO STANK AND TOOTS' LUNCHTIME SHOWDOWN

When lunchtime came around, Toots asked Whoo Stank if he wanted to join him and their classmates for lunch. Whoo Stank's heart lifted at the thought of making more friends, but as soon as Toots called out to the others, he heard a chorus of "Ew!" and "No way!" from the other animals.

"I don't want to sit next to him. His lunch will stink!" a squirrel said, wrinkling her nose.

Whoo Stank's ears drooped as he picked up his lunchbox and started to head out of the classroom. He couldn't help feeling a little hurt that no one wanted to eat with him.

But just as he was about to turn the corner, he heard a cheerful voice calling out to him. "Hey, Whoo Stank, wait up!" It was Toots.

Whoo Stank turned around to see Toots waddling up to him, a big smile on his face. "I brought my lunch, too," he said, holding up a small bag of fruit. "Let's eat together!"

Whoo Stank couldn't help but smile at Toots' kind gesture. Together, they found a quiet spot under a tree and settled down to enjoy their lunches. As they ate, Toots chatted away, "Hey, whoo Stank, what do you call a crocodile that plays the guitar?" "What?" "A ROCKodile!" they both laughed.

Whoo Stank found himself laughing and joking along with Toots, forgetting all about the other animals who had rejected him.

Whoo Stank and Toots continued to enjoy their lunch under the tree, chatting and laughing together. But just as they were finishing up, a figure loomed over them. It was Fangor, the school bully, a mean-spirited fox who loved to pick on anyone who was different.

"Ha! Look who it is, Whoo Stank the stinky skunk and his little crocodile friend," Fangor sneered. "What are you doing, eating lunch together? No one wants to be friends with you, Whoo Stank. You're a freak."

Toots stood up, puffing out his chest. "Hey, leave him alone!" he said bravely.

But Fangor just laughed. "Or what, you'll cry?" he taunted. "Crocodiles are supposed to be tough, aren't they?"

Whoo Stank felt a lump form in his throat as he watched Fangor mock Toots. He wanted to stand up for his friend, but he was too scared. What if Fangor started making fun of him too?

But just as Whoo Stank was about to back away, he felt a warm presence beside him. It was Toots, standing tall and strong.

"You might think you're tough, Fangor, but you're not," Toots said, his voice steady. "Real strength comes from accepting and supporting others, no matter who they are."

Fangor scowled, but Whoo Stank could see the doubt in his eyes. He knew that Toots' words had struck a nerve.

And just like that, Fangor slunk away, muttering under his breath. Whoo Stank and Toots breathed a sigh of relief as they watched him go.

"Thanks, Toots," Whoo Stank said, feeling grateful for his brave friend.

Toots just grinned. "That's what friends are for, Whoo Stank."

A Helping Hand

Days passed by, and Whoo Stank and Toots became inseparable. They would sit together in class, eat lunch together under the big tree outside, and play together during recess.

Despite this, Whoo Stank still couldn't help but feel the disapproving glares from the other animals. They would whisper behind his back and avoid him whenever they could.

It made Whoo Stank feel sad and alone at times. But he always tried to focus on the positive things in his life, like his friendship with Toots and his supportive teacher.

One day, as Whoo Stank was lying in his mother's lap, he opened up to her about how he was feeling demotivated by the other animals' behaviors.

His mother listened patiently and then spoke softly, "My dear Whoo Stank, sometimes when you're unique or different, others feel scared of you. They don't know how to react or understand your differences. But you mustn't let that get to you. Stay true to yourself, and don't change who you are just to please others."

Whoo Stank thought about his mother's words and felt comforted. He realized that he didn't need the approval of others to be happy. He had his own unique qualities that made him special.

As the days went on, Whoo Stank started to feel more confident in himself. He didn't let the disapproving looks and whispers of the other animals get to him anymore. He continued to be himself, and that made him happy.

Even though the other animals still didn't accept him fully, Whoo Stank knew he had his best friend, Toots, and his loving mother who believed in him. And that was enough for him.

Whoo Stank was on his way back to school after a fun weekend spent with his family. As he was walking, he saw a group of animals gathered around a small hedgehog, taunting him and making fun of him because of his prickly spines.

Whoo Stank felt a pang of sadness in his chest as he remembered how it felt to be bullied and picked on. He knew he had to help, but he was afraid of what the other animals would say or do to him.

But then he remembered the lessons his mother and teacher had taught him. He took a deep breath and walked up to the group of animals.

"Excuse me," Whoo Stank said in a calm and polite voice. "I don't think it's right to pick on someone just because they're different. Can you please leave him alone?"

The animals just laughed at Whoo Stank, making fun of his unusual smell. Whoo Stank didn't know what to do, but then he had an idea.

He stepped back and got into a position as if he was about to spray them with his scent. "I warn you, if you don't stop, I'll spray you all!" he threatened.

The other animals looked scared now and quickly backed away, and within a minute, they were all gone. Whoo Stank turned to the hedgehog, who was lying on the ground, and helped him to his feet. The hedgehog introduced himself as Cootie and thanked Whoo Stank for his braveness, and he also said how he would never be able to show such braveness.

Whoo Stank felt his chest puff up with pride as he walked home. He had stood up to the bullies and helped someone who needed it, even though it was scary. As he walked, he realized something important. What he thought was his weakness was actually his strength. His spray had always made him feel different and awkward, but in that moment, it had given him the power to help someone else.

Whoo Stank's heart swelled with newfound confidence. He realized that everyone has something that makes them unique, and it's up to us to turn those differences into strengths, just like how his spray, which he once thought was a weakness, had helped him stand up to the bullies and help Cootie, the new hedgehog at school.

As he reached home, Whoo Stank ran into his mother's lap and excitedly told her everything that had happened. She hugged him tightly and told him how proud she was of him. She also reminded him that being different is a strength, not a weakness and that we should embrace our unique qualities instead of hiding them.

Whoo Stank went to bed that night with a new sense of pride and confidence. He had learned that we should never be afraid to be ourselves and use our unique qualities to help others. And with his new friend Toots by his side, he knew that he could take on anything that came his way.

THE THREE MUSKETEERS

Whoo Stank, Toots, and Cootie quickly became inseparable friends. They would spend their days exploring the forest, having picnics by the lake, and even going on little adventures. Even though they were all different from one another, they never let their differences get in the way of their friendship.

But not everyone was happy about their newfound bond. The other animals in the school started to feel jealous and excluded. They couldn't understand how three animals who were so different could become such good friends.

And then there was Fangor, the school bully. He had always had a problem with Whoo Stank, but now that Whoo Stank had made new friends, Fangor was even more determined to make his life miserable.

Whoo Stank tried his best to ignore Fangor's taunts and insults, but it wasn't easy. One day, Fangor came up with a plan to break up their friendship once and for all. Whoo Stank knew that he needed to be strong and stand up for his friends, but he wasn't sure if he could handle Fangor on his own.

Despite the challenges they faced, Whoo Stank, Toots, and Cootie remained close. They knew that their friendship was special and worth protecting. And little did they know they were about to face their greatest challenge yet.

One day, Whoo Stank, Toots, and Cootie were playing in the park, enjoying a game of tag, when Fangor appeared out of nowhere. He had a wicked grin on his face and was flanked by his gang of cronies.

"Well, well, well, if it isn't the three musketeers," Fangor sneered, his eyes fixed on Whoo Stank. "What's the matter, Whoo Stank? Are you too scared to play with us?"

Whoo Stank tried to ignore Fangor, but he could feel his heart racing. He knew that Fangor was up to no good.

Ignoring Whoo Stank's silence, Fangor announced that he had a plan to break up their friendship once and for all.

"You see, I've got a little challenge for you," he said, his voice dripping with malice. "If you guys can make it through my obstacle course, I'll leave you alone. But if you fail, you'll have to stay away from each other forever."

The three friends looked at each other skeptically. They knew that Fangor was up to something.

But they decided to go along with the challenge, thinking that it couldn't be that hard. Oh, how wrong they were.

The next day, they showed up at the designated spot and found a twisted maze of ropes, hurdles, and obstacles that looked like it was straight out of a jungle. Fangor and his cronies were waiting for them, snickering at the sight of their challengers.

With a deep breath, Whoo Stank stepped forward, determined to show Fangor that he was not to be messed with. But as soon as he took his first step, he felt a twinge in his leg. It had been acting up lately, and he had been trying to ignore it.

Ignoring the pain, Whoo Stank pushed forward, but his leg soon gave out, and he fell to the ground, unable to get up.

Toots and Cootie rushed to his side, but Fangor and his gang laughed and jeered at them, taunting them to continue the challenge without Whoo Stank.

With tears in his eyes, Whoo Stank told his friends to go on without him, but Toots and Cootie refused. They knew that they were in this together.

Suddenly, Toots had an idea. He had been practicing his swimming skills and knew that he could swim through the underwater obstacle course without any trouble.

With Whoo Stank on his back and Cootie by his side, Toots dove into the water, determined to make it through the course.

The trio worked together, supporting each other through each obstacle until they finally made it to the end.

Fangor and his cronies were stunned. They had never seen such a display of teamwork and friendship. And as they walked away in defeat, Whoo Stank, Toots, and Cootie knew that their friendship had only grown stronger.

A Surprise Pairing

As the days went by, Whoo Stank, Toots, and Cootie's bond grew stronger. They had many adventures together, exploring new places, trying out new foods, and playing exciting games. Toots even taught Whoo Stank and Cootie how to swim in the nearby lake, which was a big accomplishment for both of them.

The school year was passing by smoothly, and classes were always fun with Miss Ollie's creative and engaging teaching methods. However, Whoo Stank still struggled with the constant exclusion and negativity he faced from the other animals. Despite this, he remained positive and grateful for his two best friends.

One day, Miss Ollie announced a new class activity that would require everyone to pair up with someone they were not already friends with. Whoo Stank immediately felt a knot form in his stomach. He knew that he was the last animal anyone would want to pair up with, and the thought of being left out was unbearable.

Miss Ollie, sensing Whoo Stank's unease, decided to spice things up a bit by playing a little game to select the partners. Each student had to draw a chit from a bowl, and whoever's name they got would be their partner for the project. The excitement in the room was palpable as everyone waited with bated breath to see who they would be paired with.

Whoo Stank breathed a sigh of relief, feeling hopeful that he might get paired with one of his dear friends. But, as the game progressed, he watched his friends being picked one by one, leaving him with no choice but to wait for his turn.

Finally, it was Whoo Stank's turn, and all eyes were on him as he drew his chit. The hushed whispers of the others echoed through the classroom as they anticipated what would be written on the little piece of paper.

Whoo Stank was surprised at what he saw; he was paired with a bobcat named Samantha. Samantha was famous for being a little intimidating because of her sharp claws and quick reflexes.

Whoo Stank felt a mix of emotions. On the one hand, he was happy to have a partner, but on the other hand, he was a little scared of Samantha. He didn't know how to talk to her or how to work with her. He worried that she would judge him for being different.

But then he remembered the words of his mother and Miss Ollie. He took a deep breath and decided to approach Samantha with a smile. "Hey, Samantha," he said. "I'm Whoo Stank. Nice to meet you."

Samantha looked at him for a moment and then smiled back. "Hi, Whoo Stank," she said. "Nice to meet you too."

From that moment on, Whoo Stank and Samantha worked together on the project, and Whoo Stank was surprised to discover that Samantha was actually a lot of fun to be around. They had their differences and argued on various things but Samantha was never mean to Whoo Stank. She was sharp-witted and funny, and she had a lot of interesting things to say. Whoo Stank also found that he could teach her a few things, like how to use his sense of smell to find hidden objects.

As they worked on the project, Whoo Stank realized that he had made a new friend. And when they presented their work to the class, Whoo Stank was proud to stand beside Samantha and show everyone what they had accomplished. He knew that their differences didn't matter and that they had both learned a valuable lesson about the power of friendship.

The next day at school, Fangor the red fox couldn't help but feel jealous when he saw Whoo Stank, Cootie, and Samantha having fun together during lunch break. He knew he couldn't stand the thought of someone else stealing his spotlight as the school's most popular animal.

So, when he saw Samantha walking towards him, he thought it was the perfect opportunity to break Whoo Stank's newfound friendship. In front of everyone, he said mean things about Whoo Stank and asked Samantha to stop being friends with him.

But to Fangor's surprise, Samantha stood up for Whoo Stank. She firmly told Fangor that being different is not a crime and that everyone has the right to live their lives without being judged or discriminated against. Fangor stormed off, still angry and jealous. Everyone, including Whoo Stank was shocked after hearing what Samantha said, but she just picked up her bag and started walking Whoo Stank was still in shock when he heard Samantha's voice, "see you tomorrow Whoo Stank".

Whoo Stank couldn't wait to tell his mother about the project and how Samantha defended him from Fangor's mean words. His mother listened quietly for a moment and then spoke, "My dear Whoo Stank, it's wonderful to have friends who accept you for who you are, but you must remember that your worth is not measured by how others treat you. You will encounter many people in your life who are not kind, and it's important to be strong and stand up for what's right and especially for yourself, even if it's not popular. Remember, you are unique and special just the way you are, and you should be proud of yourself, just like your father."

Whoo Stank didn't quite understand what his mother meant, and he asked her to explain. She replied, "You see, Whoo Stank, in life, you will face many challenges and obstacles, and not everyone will treat you with kindness or acceptance. But that doesn't mean you're not a valuable and wonderful person. You have to be brave and believe in yourself, even when others don't."

Whoo Stank was still a bit confused, but all he cared about was how Samantha defended him in front of everyone, and it made him happy. Whoo Stank smiled and went to bed that night feeling excited.

LEMONADE AND SNACKS: FRIENDS AND STUDY BUDDIES

As the school year progressed, exams were nearing, and the pressure was building up. Whoo Stank and his friends, Toots and Cootie, knew they had to work hard to do well in their exams. They decided to start studying together after school. They found the perfect spot to study - a beautiful freshwater lake in the heart of the swamp.

Every day after school, they would gather by the lake and open their textbooks. They helped each other with difficult subjects and made sure everyone understood the lessons. They also brought delicious homemade snacks that they shared while studying. Whoo Stank's mom always made him her famous carrot muffins, Toots brought crispy apple slices, and Cootie's mom made the most delicious peanut butter cookies.

The atmosphere was calm and serene by the lake, and it helped them focus better. They would take small breaks to dip their feet in the cool water and refresh themselves with some cool lemonade. As they studied, they also shared funny stories and jokes, making it a fun learning experience.

With each passing day, they felt more confident about their studies. They knew they had each other's backs and that they could count on their friendship. They even made a pact to help each other during the exams and not let the pressure get to them.

The days went by quickly, and before they knew it, the exams were upon them. But Whoo Stank and his friends were well-prepared and confident, thanks to their daily study sessions by the lake.

As Whoo Stank walked towards the school hall with his parents, he felt as if every eye in the room was on him. He was nervous about how he would be treated by the other parents, who had probably heard about his differences from their own kids. But Whoo Stank's parents were beaming with pride, excited to see their little one shine.

Suddenly, Whoo Stank heard Toots' voice from behind and turned to see his friends, who were all there with their own parents. Whoo Stank's parents greeted Toots' parents, and they all took their seats together in the hall. Whoo Stank still felt anxious, but having his friends and family with him made him feel a little better.

As the results were announced, Whoo Stank's heart was racing. He couldn't believe it when the principal called out his name as the top student in the entire school. The room fell silent, and Whoo Stank was sure that everyone was judging him for his differences.

But then, Toots started clapping, and soon Cootie and Samantha joined in. The other parents and students followed suit, and even Miss Ollie had tears in her eyes. Whoo Stank's parents were the happiest of all, hugging him tightly and congratulating him on his achievement.

Tears rolled from Whoo Stank's eyes as he went to the stage to get his award, his parent's eyes shining with happy tears in them. Whoo Stank thanked his parents, Miss Ollie, and all of his friends.

But not everyone was happy. Fangor had failed the class, and his parents were furious. They blamed Whoo Stank for their son's failure and started insulting Whoo Stank's parents. They said mean things and called them names. But Whoo Stank's parents didn't let the negativity get to them. They stayed calm and collected and didn't let the hurtful words affect them.

In the end, Whoo Stank's parents had a powerful message for Fangor's parents. They said that their son's negative attitude was a reflection of their parenting and that they should be more accepting of others.

Whoo Stank was feeling both proud and sad at the same time as he walked out of the school with his parents. He was proud of his achievement but sad that Fangor's parents were so mean to his own parents. As they were walking, his parents could see the sadness in Whoo Stank's eyes. Suddenly, Whoo Stank's mom remembered that Whoo Stank loved to sing, so she started singing his favorite song.

"Whoo Stank Skunk, he's number one, he's the best student, he's so much fun! He studied hard, and he aced the test. He's a skunk who is truly the best!"

As soon as Whoo Stank's mom started singing, Whoo Stank's dad joined in, and soon, all three of them were singing and dancing on the way back home. They had brought Whoo Stank's favorite snacks, and they were all munching on them happily. Whoo Stank felt better, and he smiled, realizing that his parents loved him no matter what.

They continued to sing and dance all the way home, and Whoo Stank felt like the happiest skunk in the world. Even though some people might not like him because he was different, he knew that he had his family.

WHOO STANK'S COLORFUL VACATION

Whoo Stank was ecstatic as he packed his bags to go to his grandparents' house for the summer. He couldn't wait to see his grandparents, who he affectionately called Grandpappy and Granny Skunk, and spend time in their unique home. Their house was built inside a giant hollow tree and had branches and leaves growing through the walls, giving it a magical and whimsical appearance.

As Whoo Stank and his father drove down the winding road, they finally arrived at his grandparents' house. Grandpappy and Granny Skunk welcomed Whoo Stank with open arms and showered him with hugs and kisses. Their jolly nature immediately put Whoo Stank at ease, and he was ready to enjoy his vacation.

A few days into his vacation, Grandpappy and Granny Sparkle decided to throw a tea party for all their skunk friends.

They welcomed them with open arms and immediately began to plan a tea party for all of their skunk friends. Whoo Stank was amazed to see so many skunks of different colors and patterns, all dressed up in their most colorful and fun outfits.

The tea party was a sight to behold. The skunks were all laughing, playing games, and enjoying the delicious food that Grandma Sparkle had prepared. Whoo Stank felt like he belonged here, among these carefree and happy skunks who didn't care about how others saw them. They were all enjoying life to the fullest, and it was infectious.

Whoo Stank felt grateful to have such wonderful grandparents and friends. Even though he was far away from his parents and old friends, he felt like he had found a new family. And as the party came to an end, and Whoo Stank bid farewell to his new friends, he knew that he would always cherish this experience and keep the memories close to his heart.

Later that night Whoo Stank lay on the grassy patch outside his grandparents' home, gazing up at the night sky. The stars twinkled brightly, like tiny diamonds scattered across a black velvet blanket. The air was cool and refreshing, carrying with it the sweet scent of flowers and the sound of crickets chirping in the distance. Whoo Stank felt a sense of calm wash over him as though the peacefulness of the night had seeped into his very being.

As he lay there, lost in thought, his Grandpappy joined him. He sat down beside Whoo Stank, his warm presence comforting in the darkness.

"What's on your mind, young one?" he asked, a gentle smile on his face.

Whoo Stank took a deep breath and began to pour out his worries and fears. He spoke of the anxiety he felt at school, of the bullying, and the fear of not being accepted. He spoke of his friends and how much they meant to him, but how he still felt like an outsider.

His grandfather listened patiently, his eyes twinkling with understanding. When Whoo Stank finished, he spoke.

"My dear Whoo Stank, you are too young to worry about every moment of your life. With time, you will learn valuable lessons, and you will find acceptance. But for now, know that you are loved and valued just the way you are. You don't have to change for anyone, and you don't have to worry about what others think of you. You have a kind heart and a beautiful soul, and that's all that matters."

As Whoo Stank listened to his grandfather's words, he felt a sense of peace settle over him.

The next morning, Whoo Stank woke up to the sweet aroma of fresh pancakes and hot chocolate. Grandpa and Grandma had prepared a delicious breakfast for him. After breakfast, they took him on a tour of their unique and colorful house. The walls were painted in bright hues of purple, green, and blue, and there were many interesting pieces of art and sculptures.

Whoo Stank was having too much fun, But it was time to go back to his own town, back to his old school, back to his old friends. Whoo Stank was feeling anxious again, wondering if things would be different this time. Grandpappy noticed the sadness on Whoo Stank's face and tried to lighten the mood with his jokes.

"Hey, Whoo Stank, why don't skunks wear perfume?" Grandpappy asked.

"I don't know, why?" Whoo Stank replied, curious.

"Because they're already scent-sational!" Grandpappy exclaimed, causing both of them to laugh.

The journey back home seemed shorter with Grandpappy's jokes and Whoo Stank's laughter. When they reached home, Whoo Stank was surprised to see his old friends, Toots, Cootie, and Samantha, waiting for him outside his house with balloons and banners, welcoming him back.

Whoo Stank couldn't believe his eyes and was overjoyed to see his friends welcoming him with open arms. Toots explained that they had missed him a lot and wanted to surprise him with a welcome-back party.

As they entered Whoo Stank's house, they saw Whoo Stank's parents setting up a table with Whoo Stank's favorite snacks and drinks. Whoo Stank's mother hugged him tightly, telling him how proud she was of him, and Whoo Stank's father ruffled his hair, telling him how much he had grown in just a few weeks.

Whoo Stank realized that he had made many good memories during his vacations with his grandparents, but he also realized that he had made many more good memories with his old friends.

UNBREAKABLE BONDS

As the school year began, Whoo Stank and his friends were filled with excitement and anticipation. They were entering their senior year, ready for more fun and adventures together. However, little did they know that Fangor the fox was plotting his revenge against Whoo stank for outshining him in the previous year's exams. Whoo Stank's parents had tried to reason with Fangor's parents, but it seemed that their efforts had only fueled Fangor's anger further.

To start the year off on a positive note, Whoo Stank and his friends decided to go to school together on the first day. They gathered at Whoo Stank's house, where his mother had prepared a delightful breakfast for everyone. Laughter and joy filled the air as they made their way to school, with Toots sharing his hilarious jokes along the journey.

As they reached the school and entered their classroom, Whoo Stank's heart sank when he saw Fangor standing with a group of classmates, all staring at him. The moment Whoo Stank stepped in, Fangor pretended to gag, creating a dramatic show of a foul smell, which made everyone burst into laughter. Whoo Stank was taken aback, his anxiety growing stronger. Toots immediately stepped up to defend Whoo Stank, urging Fangor to stop acting like a child and go to his own class. But Toots couldn't resist adding a sarcastic remark, reminding Fangor that he was in their class because he had failed the previous year. Fangor turned red with embarrassment and frustration, his anger boiling over. He lunged toward Toots, ready to attack, but Samantha swiftly stepped in between, warning Fangor not to mess with her friends.

Amidst the chaos, a teacher entered the classroom and commanded everyone to take their seats. Whoo Stank, still upset by the incident, was comforted by Toots, who held his hand and guided him to his seat. Despite the unfortunate start, Whoo Stank knew that he had true friends by his side who would always support and defend him.

As the class settled down, a new teacher Mr. Piggles entered the room. He was a pig with a round, jolly face and wore a vibrant bowtie that matched his colorful attire. Mr. Piggles sensed the tension in the classroom, aware that Whoo Stank's uniqueness had made him a target of judgment. However, he chose not to address it directly, understanding that Whoo Stank needed to learn to fight his own battles and grow stronger from within.

With a smile, Mr. Piggles announced that his teaching method would be different from what the students were accustomed to. Throughout the school year, they would be performing tasks and assignments in pairs. Excitement filled the room as everyone started looking for their preferred partners. However, the teacher interrupted, stating that he would be the one to decide the pairs.

To everyone's shock, the teacher pointed at Whoo Stank and Fangor, pairing them together. Whoo Stank's heart sank, feeling disrupted by the news, while Fangor wore a cunning smile on his face. Whoo stank mustered up the courage to approach the teacher after class, explaining that Fangor bullied him and requesting a change in his group. But the teacher, wise and understanding, responded with a gentle but firm voice.

"Whoo Stank," Mr. Piggles said, placing a hand on Whoo Stank's shoulder, "life won't always be in your favor. If you remain within your comfort zone, you'll be stuck there forever. How long can others continue to stand up for you if you don't learn to stand up for yourself?"

Whoo Stank's eyes widened as he took in Mr. Piggles words. The truth resonated within him, and he realized that it was time to face his fears and confront his challenges head-on. The teacher's advice sparked a fire within Whoo stank, igniting a newfound determination to overcome his anxieties and embrace his uniqueness with confidence.

As Whoo Stank walked, deep in thought about Mr. Piggles' words, he couldn't shake off the lingering doubt about how he would handle being paired with Fangor for the entire year. Lost in his thoughts, Whoo Stank was surprised when his friends, Toots, Cootie, and Samantha, caught up with him. Concerned expressions filled their faces as they listened to Whoo Stank's worries.

With unwavering support, Toots stepped forward and placed a paw on Whoo Stank's shoulder. "Whoo Stank," he said with a reassuring smile, "don't let this bring you down. You are capable of anything, and together, we can face any challenge that comes our way."

Cootie chimed in, her voice filled with determination. "Remember, Whoo Stank, we are here for you. We've seen your strength and courage, and we believe in you. You've overcome so much already, and this is just another hurdle to conquer."

Samantha nodded in agreement, her eyes filled with warmth and encouragement. "Whoo Stank, you are unique, and that's what makes you special. Don't let anyone make you feel inferior. Stand tall, be proud of who you are, and don't let anyone's negativity bring you down."

Whoo Stank looked at his friends, their unwavering support shining through their words and expressions. In that moment, he felt a surge of strength and determination welling up within him. He realized that he wasn't alone in this journey; he had a support system that believed in him and his abilities.

With newfound confidence, Whoo Stank straightened his posture, a glimmer of determination gleaming in his eyes. "You're right," he said, his voice filled with conviction. "I won't let this bring me down. Together, we can face anything. Thank you, my friends, for always being there for me."

And so, with their support and the fire of determination burning bright within him, Whoo Stank marched forward, ready to embrace the challenges that lay ahead, knowing that with his friends by his side, he could conquer anything that came their way.

UNVEILING UNIQUENESS

As Whoo Stank and Fangor sat side by side, the air between them crackled with tension. Fangor couldn't resist making snide remarks, trying to provoke Whoo Stank. But Whoo Stank had made up his mind to stay focused and not let Fangor's negativity distract him.

Mr. Piggles stood at the front of the class, his warm gaze sweeping across the room. He explained the first task, a unique opportunity for each pair to discover and appreciate the qualities that made their partner special. The task involved learning about their families, their backgrounds, and what made them who they were.

Whoo Stank turned to Fangor, determined to make the best of the situation. "Fangor," he began, his voice steady, "tell me about your family. What are some things that make them unique?"

Fangor scoffed, clearly uncomfortable with the idea of sharing. But Whoo Stank's unwavering kindness and genuine interest broke through Fangor's defensive wall. Reluctantly, Fangor started talking about his family's love for storytelling, their talent for painting beautiful landscapes, and their tradition of hosting community events.

Whoo Stank listened attentively, genuinely intrigued by the aspects of Fangor's family that he had never known before. He reciprocated by sharing stories about his own family's love for music, their knack for baking mouthwatering treats, and their passion for gardening.

As the task continued, Whoo Stank and Fangor discovered more about each other's unique qualities. Whoo Stank learned about Fangor's skill in building intricate structures with sticks and stones, while Fangor discovered Whoo Stank's talent for solving puzzles and creating imaginative stories.

With each revelation, a newfound understanding and respect blossomed between Whoo Stank and Fangor. They realized that despite their differences, there was beauty and value in embracing the uniqueness of others. Mr. Piggles' task was teaching them a valuable lesson about acceptance and finding common ground.

As the class session came to an end, Whoo Stank and Fangor exchanged a hesitant but genuine smile. They had discovered something remarkable about each other – beneath the surface, they were not so different after all.

A Scent Of Courage

As the days passed, Fangor found himself slowly getting to know Whoo Stank on a deeper level. He felt a growing sense of remorse for his past behavior and a desire to apologize. But his ego and fear of judgment held him back. What would his friends and family think if he suddenly became friends with Whoo Stank? Fangor was torn and unsure of what to do.

One day, as Fangor made his way to class, his bully friends approached him, questioning why he hadn't played a prank on Whoo Stank in a long time. Fearful of revealing his changing feelings towards Whoo Stank, Fangor pretended to be in agreement and promised them that he would soon pull another prank.

In class, Fangor's demeanor changed, and he became cold and mean towards Whoo Stank. He didn't want to show his vulnerability or risk being ridiculed by his friends and family. Whoo Stank noticed the sudden change and approached Fangor, genuinely concerned.

"Is everything okay, Fangor?" Whoo Stank asked, his voice filled with worry.

Fangor, caught off guard, lashed out at Whoo Stank, choosing meanness as a defense mechanism. It was easier for Fangor to be mean than to reveal his true feelings. Whoo Stank fell silent, hurt by Fangor's words.

Mr. Piggles, the observant teacher, noticed the tension between the two and decided to intervene. After class, he called Fangor aside and asked him about his behavior. Fangor hesitated at first, but then opened up to Mr. Piggles, sharing his fears and struggles.

"Fangor," Mr. Piggles began gently, "when we choose to change for the better, it's natural to feel scared and uncertain. But taking that first step out of your comfort zone is crucial for personal growth. You don't want to remain stuck in negativity forever. It's time to break free."

Fueled by Mr. Piggles' words, Fangor mustered up the courage to make amends. He ran towards the exit where Whoo Stank and his friends were leaving for the weekend picnic. Panting for breath, Fangor approached Whoo Stank, offering a heartfelt apology. Whoo Stank, with a forgiving smile, accepted it graciously.

Toots, ever the joyful friend, invited Fangor to join them on their weekend adventure. The group gathered their favorite snacks, including Toots' legendary cheesy puffs, Samantha's homemade chocolate chip cookies, and Whoo Stank's refreshing lemonade. Cootie brought a cozy blanket for them to relax on.

They set off, walking through a lush forest, the colorful attire of Whoo Stank and his friends brightening up the path. Laughter filled the air as they played with a bouncing ball, and Toots couldn't help but burst into spontaneous song.

After a while, they reached their picnic spot—a serene swamp surrounded by tall grasses and water lilies. It was a hidden gem, a natural haven for their adventure. They played games, enjoyed their snacks, and took refreshing dips in the cool lake.

Suddenly, Fangor's mean-spirited friends arrived, their mocking words slicing through the air. Fangor felt a surge of fear, but this time it wasn't for himself—it was for Whoo Stank and his friends. He urged them to stay away, knowing the danger that lurked.

But the bullies refused to listen, launching an attack. They pushed and struck, creating chaos and spreading hate. In that moment, Whoo Stank remembered the courage instilled in him by his parents and grandparents. He knew it was time to take a stand.

Drawing upon the strength he had discovered within himself, Whoo Stank surged forward, his instincts taking over. With a swift, instinctive movement, he unleashed his natural defense mechanism: a powerful spray that sent one of Fangor's friends reeling backward, clutching his stinging eyes. The air was filled with a fragrance as delightful as a blossoming garden, leaving everyone astonished.

Fangor, frozen in disbelief, watched as Whoo Stank's friends rallied beside him, joining the battle against the tormentors. Together, they stood against hate and injustice, their unity a force to be reckoned with.

Overwhelmed by the unexpected resistance, Fangor's friends soon realized they were no match for the strength of genuine friendship. In a hasty retreat, they vanished into the depths of the forest, their harmful intentions defeated.

As the dust settled, Whoo Stank's friends gathered around him, their expressions a mix of awe and concern. Inquisitive gazes turned to Whoo Stank, as they questioned how he had conjured such a captivating aroma and defended them all. Whoo Stank, his eyes reflecting a sense of newfound self-acceptance, confessed that this was a truth he had never shared with anyone before—a truth he had kept hidden.

With empathy and understanding, Whoo Stank's friends embraced him, offering support and gratitude for his courage. Fangor, touched by Whoo Stank's bravery and the realization that hate and prejudice had clouded his judgment, approached Whoo Stank with tears streaming down his face. Through choked sobs, Fangor pleaded for forgiveness, burdened by the weight of his past actions.

In that moment, Whoo Stank gazed into Fangor's remorseful eyes and found it in his heart to grant forgiveness. Understanding the transformative power of growth and redemption, Whoo Stank embraced Fangor, the warmth of their reconciliation a beacon of hope for a future free from animosity.

As the group basked in the aftermath of the conflict, their bond grew stronger. Laughter and chatter filled the air once again, replacing the echoes of hatred. The fragrance of acceptance and unity enveloped them, a testament to the resilience of friendship and the power of understanding.

Whoo Stank realized that beneath the surface, they were all the same—vulnerable, capable of change, and yearning for connection. It was the prejudices instilled by society that twisted their perceptions and turned them into instruments of division. But in that moment of revelation, Whoo Stank understood that the path to harmony begins with acknowledging our shared humanity and defying the chains of prejudice.

And so, as the sun dipped below the horizon, casting its golden hues across the tranquil swamp, Whoo Stank, Fangor, and their friends rejoiced in the newfound harmony that had emerged from the ashes of adversity. They understood that their journey together had just begun, that the battles they faced were not merely physical but fought on the fronts of compassion, acceptance, and growth.

In the end, it was their collective courage that transformed their lives, forever weaving their destinies together as allies in the pursuit of a more compassionate world—a world where differences were celebrated, friendships were forged, and hate had no place to thrive.

EPILOGUE: A SONG OF FRIENDSHIP

In the days that followed the incident at the picnic, a remarkable transformation took place within the school. The once divided corridors were now filled with laughter, camaraderie, and the sweet scent of friendship. Whoo Stank, Fangor, and their friends had learned valuable lessons about acceptance, compassion, and the strength that lies in unity.

As their senior year progressed, Whoo Stank, Fangor, and their friends studied diligently, supporting and encouraging one another every step of the way. They formed study groups, shared knowledge, and embraced their unique talents. With determination and perseverance, they overcame academic challenges, each achieving excellent grades.

On the day of the final exams, excitement and nerves filled the air. Whoo Stank and Fangor exchanged reassuring smiles, knowing that they had grown beyond their past differences. They approached the exams with confidence, knowing that their true strength lay not only in their individual abilities but also in their unwavering support for one another.

When the results were announced, a wave of celebration rippled through the school. Whoo Stank, Fangor, and their friends had all excelled, surpassing expectations and proving their dedication. They stood together, proud of their achievements and grateful for the bonds they had forged.

In the closing moments of their school journey, as the sun began to set, the school courtyard came alive with joyful voices. Whoo Stank, Fangor, and their friends gathered in a circle, their arms around each other, swaying gently to a tune that echoed the spirit of their shared experiences. They sang:

We walked a path with bumps and bends,

Where friendships grew, and hate did mend.

Through trials faced, we stood as one,

In unity, our journey won.

Oh, let the world see the power of friends,

Where love and acceptance never end.

We'll shine our light, breaking barriers tall,

In friendship's embrace, we stand proud and tall.

Skunks and foxes, side by side,

In unity, we set the tide.

From prejudice, we break the chain,

In hearts united, love shall remain.

Oh, let the world see the power of friends,

Where love and acceptance never end.

We'll shine our light, breaking barriers tall,

In friendship's embrace, we stand proud and tall.

As their voices harmonized, the echoes of their song spread far and wide, touching the hearts of those who listened. Whoo Stank, Fangor, and their friends knew that their journey had just begun, and they vowed to carry the lessons they had learned into the world beyond.

And so, with hearts full of gratitude, they bid farewell to their beloved school, confident in the knowledge that their bond would endure, forever reminding them of the power of friendship and the strength that lies in embracing one another's differences.

The End

Made in the USA
Las Vegas, NV
11 January 2024

84246593R00026